CW00589775

The First Colour Motion Pictures

1 Charles Urban

The First Colour Motion Pictures

D B Thomas BSc PhD

LONDON   HER MAJESTY'S STATIONERY OFFICE

© Crown copyright 1969
First published 1969
Second impression 1983

Cover From a coloured
Kinemacolor lantern slide

ISBN 0 11 290014 3

Preface to the 1983 Reprint

The text of this new edition is virtually unchanged
from the original written about fifteen years ago.
During that time we have received several
enquiries from readers about the location of
archives of Kinemacolor film. Unfortunately
nothing exists in the Science Museum collections
and only short excerpts from the large amount of
film which must once have existed appear to
have been preserved in the national archives.
It seems that we will never see the Delhi Durbar
of 1911 in colour again, or indeed any other major
Kinemacolor production.

David Thomas
Keeper
Department of Physics

Foreword

There have been over a hundred processes devised for producing motion pictures in natural colour, and the names given to them range through the alphabet from Agfacolor to Zoechrome. Only a few of these processes had any considerable success; indeed not many of them reached the stage of being seen on the screen of the local cinema. Before 1920 there was only one natural colour process, Kinemacolor, which was a commercial success and which reached most of the cities and towns of Britain. About a million feet of negative film stock went through the Kinemacolor cameras.

Kinemacolor, invented by G A Smith, was simple compared to later processes and it had several serious limitations. It succeeded because of the enterprise of Charles Urban, an *entrepreneur* with little technical knowledge. It was he who presented Smith with the idea of inventing a process for producing motion pictures in natural colour and, once a practicable process was devised, it was he who directed the Natural Color Kinematograph Company which marketed the product.

In 1937 Urban presented a collection of documents dealing with the film industry before 1925 to the Science Museum. Dr David B Thomas, Deputy Keeper in the Department of Chemistry, has written his monograph with the help of this material.

D H Follett
Director   1969

Introduction

Before we can describe ways of making motion pictures in colour we need to understand some quite simple facts about colour itself. White light (sunlight) is made up of a spectrum of colours ranging from violet to red. If we pass sunlight through a glass prism we can view this spectrum on a sheet of paper. We can also combine the spectrum colours to produce white light making use of the phenomenon of persistence of vision. Thus if we take a circular disc and paint it with sectors representing the colours of the spectrum, on rotating the disc rapidly it will appear to be white, the combination of the colours taking place within the eye, or more correctly the brain, of the viewer.

It is an experimental fact that, for people with normal colour vision, any colour in the spectrum can be produced by mixing no more than three other colours, called the three primary colours. This idea was first expounded in the 18th century and it was suggested by Thomas Young in 1802 that the reason was to be found in the fact that the human eye has three sets of nerves, each set of which is sensitive to just one of the three colours red, green and blue.

There are two ways in which we can mix colours. Suppose we project three beams of light on to a screen. If we use a red beam, a green beam and a blue beam, where the three beams overlap we can get white light. In other words the three beams add up to white. These three colours blue, green and red are known as the additive primaries and are used in additive colour processes. The screen of a colour television set is made up of small elements of these three colours as colour television is an additive process.

If on the other hand we use just one beam of light and produce the colour by the superimposition of dyed images in front of the projector lens, then we need to use the three colours, yellow, cyan and magenta as our primaries. These three colours are known as the subtractive primaries. A modern colour film, whether still or motion picture, contains mixtures of these three dyes as colour film these days is made by subtractive processes. Yellow is white light minus blue, cyan white light minus red and magenta white light minus green.

Before Kinemacolor

Colour photography in the 19th century

Soon after photography was introduced in 1839 photographs in colour could be seen in the form of hand-painted daguerreotypes. Although there were some early experiments directed at producing photographs in colour by a natural colour process there was one insuperable difficulty – the light sensitive materials used in photography were only sensitive to a small range of colour, in fact only the blue and ultra-violet portion of the spectrum.

One of the great 19th century physicists, James Clerk Maxwell, was interested in colour and, in 1855, he suggested that Young's three colour theory, briefly mentioned in the introduction, could be used to make a colour photograph. His idea was to isolate each of the primary colours by taking three negatives, one through a green filter, one through a blue filter, and one through a red filter. Each of these three negatives, although in appearance black and white, would be a colour record of the amount of each particular colour in the original scene. Positive black and white transparencies were then to be made from these negatives and projected in register on to a screen by means of three lanterns each fitted with the appropriate filter in front of the projection lens. The combination of the three coloured images on the screen would be a true colour photograph.

This scheme was put into effect and the first results were shown at a meeting of the Royal Institution in May 1861. The photograph exhibited at the meeting was the first photograph by a natural colour process and marks the birth of colour photography. Since Maxwell produced his colour by mixing light beams this is an additive

* Journal of Photographic Science, pp. 243–246, 1961.

process and he used the three additive primaries blue, green and red.

One thing puzzled photographers for years – as the photographic plates used by Maxwell were insensitive to the red light of the spectrum, how did he manage to get an image on his plate when the plate was exposed behind the red filter. Fortunately sufficiently good experimental records were in existence for the experiment to be repeated in modern times. As a result R M Evans found in 1960* that although it was true that Maxwell's plates were quite insensitive to red light, the red filter which he used transmitted some ultra-violet rays and the red portion of the subject, a tartan ribbon, emitting some ultra-violet, made an impression on the plate. Even so, with the red filter in place Maxwell needed an extremely long exposure to produce an image of satisfactory density.

In 1873 H W Vogel made the outstanding discovery that the addition of small quantities of certain dyestuffs to photographic emulsions made the plates sensitive to a wider range of colours. The photographic images produced were still of course, black and white. During the decades which followed the discovery, the spectral sensitivity of emulsions was gradually increased until in 1906 the first panchromatic emulsions sensitive to virtually the whole of the visible spectrum were marketed. Even as early as the 1890s the increase in spectral sensitivity brought about by Vogel's discovery meant that Maxwell's process came into common usage. The three black and white photographic positives were shown either by multiple projection as in Maxwell's experiment, or by viewing them in register through filters in devices

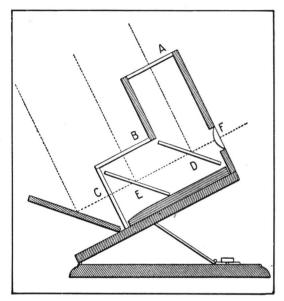

2 Sectional diagram of a
chromoscope viewer
for still colour photo-
graphs (c.1900). Three
colour records are
placed with their
appropriate red, green
or blue filter at A, B
and C respectively. By
means of the half-
silvered mirrors D and
E the user sees the
three images in colour
and in register through
the eye-piece F.

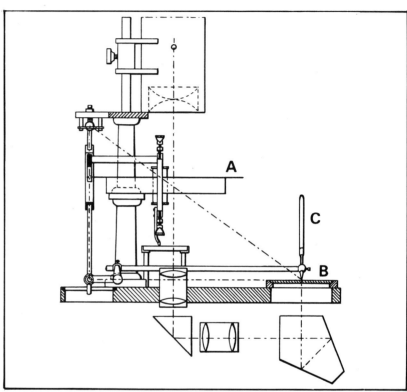

3 A stencil making mach-
ine. A magnified image
of one frame of a film
A is projected on to
ground glass at B. The
operator traces an out-
line with the rod C.
The depression of the
rod closes an electrical
circuit activating the
cutting tools.

known as chromoscopes. As three separate exposures were needed, only still-life subjects could be taken by this method at first.

Thus we see that even before the start of the cinema the basic requirements of a colour process for still photography – three records of the primary colours and a method of producing the three records in colour and in register – were widely known.

Hand-painting, stencilling, tinting and toning

Motion pictures in colour could be seen in 1896 soon after the birth of the cinema. Like the first photographs in colour, they were hand-painted. Films were shown at sixteen pictures per second and the first films, about fifty feet in length and lasting about fifty seconds, contained over 700 individual pictures. The colouring was done by women, each of whom applied one colour only. Although the work involved in hand-painting a fifty foot length of film would seem prodigious, the cost of colouring in 1902 was only 35/- per fifty feet of film on top of the usual cost at that time of 21/- for the black and white print.

By 1907 the length of the average film had increased and, with the increase in the number of cinemas, the number of copies required of each film had also increased. (Films in those days were sold out-right to each exhibitor. The hiring of films became the usual method of distribution later.) Hand-colouring soon became impracticable and a method of colouring was devised which used stencils. In general it was the French companies, particularly Pathé, which used the method. By 1910 Pathé Frères employed 400 workers entirely on hand and machine colouring at their factory at Vincennes.

The stencils (one for each colour) were made with machines which resembled pantographs. An enlarged image of one frame of the film was projected on to a ground-glass screen in front of the operator. She traced the outline of the area required to be in one particular colour. Her pencil, as it touched the glass, brought together two cutting tools on either side of the film, cutting out the stencil image. The film was then advanced one frame and the operation repeated. After the stencil had been made for the whole length of film, it was placed in contact with the film which was to be coloured, and the two films were run through a machine which applied colour through the holes in the stencil by means of a short endless band of velvet carrying the dye. The stencil-coloured films were finally retouched by hand. By means of this automation stencil-coloured films were still being produced in the 1920s. It was only worth the expense of producing a stencil when a fairly large number of copies of a film were required. This meant that stencil-colouring was particularly useful only for the more popular films. Although the method may appear rather crude the effects which could be achieved were often quite pleasing.

Colour was also introduced on to the screen by tinting the film by immersing it in a dye which was absorbed by the gelatin of the emulsion. Thus a fire scene would be tinted red, a night scene blue or a sunlit scene yellow. The dye, of course, produced a uniform tint throughout the picture.

Toning was also used on early films. The black and white photographic image consists of finely divided silver which can be converted into almost any insoluble silver salt. When the silver is con-

*Patent No. 6202 of 1899

4   The shutter of the Lee
and Turner projector
(shown overleaf). In
this photograph the
red portions of the
filters are reproduced
as dark grey, the green
portions as medium
grey and the blue
portions as light grey.

verted into a coloured salt the process is known
as 'chemical toning' and the image is produced
in the colour of the compound which replaces the
original silver. Thus if we treat a black and white
film with potassium ferrocyanide the silver is converted to blue-green silver ferrocyanide and we
get a blue-green image. By choice of reagent it is
possible to produce an image of yellow, magenta
or almost any colour. The image, being translucent,
presents a coloured image on the screen.

The difference between tinting and toning is that
tinting produces a uniform overall colour while
toning only changes the black silver image into
another colour.

The Lee and Turner process
The first natural colour process for motion pictures
was derived from Maxwell's first natural colour
process for still photographs. Maxwell had
simultaneously projected the black and white
transparencies of three colour records through the
three corresponding filters to produce a colour
photograph. Edward R Turner projected three
frames of a motion picture through filters to produce a motion picture in colour. Turner received
the financial backing of F Marshall Lee and so the
process became known as the Lee and Turner
process.

In the conventional motion picture camera the
film is moved intermittently with a rotating
shutter interrupting light passing through the lens
while the film is moving. The Lee and Turner
patent* describes such a camera in which the
shutter consists of three opaque sectors alternating
with three colour filters, red, green and blue
respectively. The shutter is synchronised so that
successive frames of the film are exposed through
red, green and blue filters. The exposed film thus
consists of a recurring series of red, green and blue
colour records, the records of the three primary
colours which are needed for any three-colour
process. Apart from the colour filter shutter the
camera as shown in the patent is conventional.
The patent does not state the number of frames
per second taken with the camera.

5 The unsuccessful Lee and Turner three-colour projector of 1901 with the three 'sawn off' lenses for simultaneous projection.

As photographic emulsions in 1899 were more sensitive to blue-violet light than to the green and red parts of the spectrum, a camera which gave equal exposures with each of the three filters in position would underexpose the green and red colour records. Lee and Turner in their patent indicated that the opaque sectors of their filter disc shutter could be increased or decreased as desired to produce the required ratio of blue, green and red exposures.

The method of projection was rather complicated. Three consecutive frames of the film were projected on to the screen simultaneously by means of three projection lenses placed very close together. Each frame of the film was projected three times, first through the upper lens, then through the middle lens, and finally through the lower lens. The colour was provided by a synchronised rotating three-sectored shutter bearing concentric bands of colour filters (as shown). Suppose we consider a red frame (one which was photographed through a red filter). When it is projected through the upper lens the beam of light passes through the outer red filter of the shutter. It is then moved down to the middle lens and projected through the middle red filter of the shutter. Through the lower lens it is projected through the inner red filter of the shutter. The film, of course, moves intermittently and while it is moving the projection light is masked by the opaque portions of the filter disc.

At first sight this method of projection may appear to be unnecessarily complicated. The same effect could have been achieved by projecting each frame once only, moving the film the length of three frames (three inches) at a time. However the strain involved in moving the film three inches intermittently would have been too great.

Later systems based on the Lee and Turner process attempted to obviate this difficulty by reducing the frame height (see page 32) or by placing the frames side by side. None of these variants which appeared 1912–1925 proved wholly successful.

During 1901 Lee withdrew his backing and Turner approached Charles Urban, at that time Managing Director of the Warwick Trading Company, one of the early British motion picture companies.

Charles Urban (1867–1942) was born in Ohio and spent his boyhood in Cincinnati. In the early 1890s he went from Ohio to Detroit and opened a stationery shop. He then became a phonograph salesman introducing the machine into offices for dictation purposes. In this way he became associated with Edison inventions and after 1894 managed a phonograph and kinetoscope parlour on Woodward Avenue, Detroit. He obtained the

6 A row of nine Edison Kinetoscopes at Urban's 'Phonograph and Kinetoscope Parlor' in Detroit, 1895.

7 Experimental Lee and Turner 38 mm film showing the unusual perforations and the colour records recurring every third frame (1901–02).

agency rights in Michigan of the Vitascope, the first American motion picture projector, in 1896. He then came to England as the London manager of Maguire and Baucus, the company marketing Edison films in England. In 1897 he renamed the London firm The Warwick Trading Company after its offices in Warwick Court. Soon after this the company began making its own films. As a result of Urban's drive the company prospered and sales rose from £10 500 in 1897 to more than £45 000 in 1901. By this time it was the leading British film company. During the Boer War Urban had three cameramen in the field filming the campaign, producing the first war films ever shown. He distributed the films of several British and French film makers including Williamson of Brighton, Méliès of Paris, Mottershaw of Sheffield, Lumière of Paris and G A Smith of Brighton. The Warwick Trading Company also marketed cameras, projectors and other motion picture apparatus much of it made by Alfred Darling of Brighton.

When Turner approached Urban with the idea for producing and exhibiting colour films, Urban took to the subject with his usual enthusiasm and his company financed Turner's work for six months. A camera for the Lee and Turner process made of aluminium was built by Darling of Brighton for the Warwick Trading Company in October 1901. A curious feature of the camera was the use of non-standard film. Instead of 1⅜ inch (35 mm), the film was 1½ inch (38 mm) in width. The perforations were round with a 1 inch pitch, two perforations appearing between each frame. A special perforating machine to produce the film was built by Darling at the same time. A three-colour projector was supplied by Darling in February 1902, but the design, manufacture and fitting of lenses was not

8 The perforator for
Lee and Turner 38 mm
film. The film was
wound between the
two cylinders, the
upper being a punch
the lower one a die.

completed until April 1902. Unfortunately Turner
died soon afterwards.

The projector was not a great success. 'As soon as
the handle of the projecting machine was worked
the three pictures refused to remain in register
and no knowledge that any of us could bring to
bear upon the matter could even begin to cure
the trouble . . . The difficulty is mainly due to the
fact that the cinematograph pictures are small to
begin with (about the size of a postage stamp),
and they have to be enormously magnified in
exhibiting, as you all know. The slightest defect in
registration is pitilessly magnified!'*

In 1902, after Turner's death, Urban acquired the
patent rights of the Lee and Turner process from
Turner's widow. Urban had insufficient technical
knowledge to conduct research on a possible
motion picture colour process, but he had one
associate, George Albert Smith, who had an
interest in science and who also had some of that
initiative which Urban expected of his employees.
Smith (1864–1959) had been a photographer in
Brighton before he took up cinematography in
1897. He produced his first films for the Warwick
Trading Company in 1898, and, in 1900, signed a
two-year exclusive contract with Urban's company for the distribution of his films.

Urban agreed to finance work by Smith on
improving the Lee and Turner process. After
November 1902 Smith and Urban decided to use
standard gauge 35 mm film and the Lee and
Turner camera made a year earlier was modified
to take the standard gauge. The three-colour
projector was clearly impracticable and a second
method of exhibiting the films was attempted.

10 George Albert Smith in his office at St. Ann's Well, Hove, 1899.

9 Urban's three-colour filter-tinting machine for 35 mm film (1902). Made by Braun and Co., King's Cross.

This involved tinting each individual frame with the appropriate colour. A frame representing the red colour record would be tinted red, the blue colour record tinted blue and the green colour record tinted green, each colour recurring with every third picture. In this way the tinted film carried its own filter and could be projected in a conventional 35 mm film projector. When projected at three times the normal speed an impression of natural colour would result from the phenomenon of persistence of vision. At lower projection speeds a three-colour sequential system like this (one which projects the three colours consecutively rather than simultaneously) produces colour flicker or pulsating colour. A tinting machine was built but it was not a success probably because of the difficulty of obtaining an even coating of dye on each frame. Also it may have been found too difficult to project the film at sufficient speed without the film breaking. This was Urban's last attempt to introduce colour on to the film itself. In all the later work with which he was associated a rotating filter disc on the projector was used as the source of colour.

As a result of these discouraging attempts at projecting a three-colour film through filters, Smith began in 1902 to devise a simplified process which resulted in the first commercially successful natural colour process for motion pictures, Kinemacolor. (As Urban was an American, the word is always spelt without a 'u'.)

11 George Albert Smith.
(by courtesy of the
National Film Archive).

Kinemacolor

The Invention of Kinemacolor

Although three colours are necessary to reproduce a scene accurately, Smith found that a two-colour process using the colours red and green could produce quite pleasing and acceptable results. This compromise immediately simplified the Lee and Turner method and formed the basis of a practicable colour process. Using just two colours instead of three the taking and projecting speeds could be reduced to 32 frames per second and this reduced both the cost of film and wear on the film in the camera and projector.

Smith further improved the Lee and Turner process by producing the first panchromatic motion picture film. Panchromatic plates for still photography were first introduced in 1906, but motion picture film at that date was still not sensitised to the whole of the spectrum. Indeed panchromatic film stock was not generally available until about 1919. Despite his lack of chemical training Smith was able to formulate a treatment of existing motion picture film which enabled him to produce a product with sufficient red sensitivity for the purpose of colour cinematography. His method was to bathe the negative film stock in a sensitising dye solution, a method which may tend to produce spots and other defects on the processed film. Panchromatic film stock is generally made by incorporating the sensitising dyes into the emulsion at the time the emulsion is prepared.

The first trial of the new process took place outside Smith's house at Southwick, Brighton. Urban recalled the occasion in the following words:* 'One Sunday we were ready for the first real two-colour test. It was a beautiful sunshiny day. Smith dressed his little boy and girl in a variety of colours, the girl was in white with a pink sash, the boy in sailor blue waving a Union Jack; We had the green grass and the red brick house for a setting. This was July 1906.

'It took about thirty seconds to make the exposure on a specially prepared negative film after which we went into Smith's small darkroom to develop the results in absolute darkness.

'Within two hours we had dried the negative, made a positive print of the 50 feet length, developed and dried it – and then for the grand test.

'Even today – after seventeen years (*sic*), I can feel the thrill of that moment, when I saw the result of the two-colour process – I yelled like a drunken cowboy – "We've got it – We've got it".'

Smith applied for a patent for the process in November 1906 (Patent No. 26671). He described the process as follows: 'An animated picture of a coloured scene is taken with a bioscope camera in the usual way, except that a revolving shutter is used fitted with properly adjusted red and green colour screens. A negative is thus obtained in which the reds and yellows are recorded in one picture, and the greens and yellows (with some blue) in the second, and so on alternately throughout the length of the bioscope film.

'A positive picture is made from the above negative and projected by the ordinary projecting machine which, however, is fitted with a revolving shutter furnished with somewhat similar coloured glasses to the above, and so contrived that the red

*Typewritten notes dated 1921 in the Science Museum Urban Collection. (The scene described here by Urban is so similar to that depicted in the *three*-colour film shown on page 7 that it seems that he may have confused the two events.)

and green pictures are projected alternately through their appropriate colour glasses.

'If the speed of projection is approximately 30 pictures per second, the two colour records blend and present to the eye a satisfactory rendering of the subject in colours which appear to be natural.

'The novelty of my method lies in the use of two colours only, red and green, combined with the principle of persistence of vision.'

The Kinemacolor filters

The degree of accuracy with which a two-colour additive process can reproduce colours depends on the precise colour transmission of the taking and projection filters. At the time of Smith's patent there were on the market tricolour filters for still colour photography transmitting red, green, and blue respectively. The patent suggests that at this time Smith was using just the red and green tricolour filters in taking and projecting Kinema-color. In practice it was found that this produced a fairly acceptable representation of colours (in rather warm tones) except for subjects predomin-antly blue such as the sky or the sea which tended to appear too dark and of an unnatural colour.

In order to produce a more acceptable colour rendering a blue-green filter (one transmitting a little blue as well as green) could be substituted for the tricolour green filter. However, a two-colour process can never reproduce all colours of the spectrum accurately – any choice of filters must be a compromise – and the increase of blue transmission of the green filter produced deterioration in the reproduction of greens.

According to one report grass and green foliage tended to be reproduced as a bronze brown.

In fact when we examine Kinemacolor apparatus we find that a number of different types of filter were used, the choice depending on the nature of the subject and the light conditions. On a dull day a very light pair of filters (a pair very lightly dyed and transmitting a high proportion of the incident light) was a necessity in order to get a negative which was not badly underexposed.

The taking filters were made either of glass or gelatin while the projection filters were of gelatin. Each projectionist was required to adjust the projection filter before use. The red section of the filter was of a single thickness of gelatin, the green section was of double thickness over part of the green area. The projectionist adjusted the area of the double thickness until the screen illumination appeared yellow-white. An orange tint on the screen indicated that the double portion of the green filter was too large; a greenish cast indicated that it was too small.

In 1910–11, when Kinemacolor was beginning to achieve success, Colin N Bennett gave assistance to the Natural Color Kinematograph Company in the design of filters. He also wrote 'On Operating Kinemacolor', a 25-page booklet of instructions for Kinemacolor exhibitors.

Exploitation of Kinemacolor in Britain

Smith and Urban had an agreement that each was to participate equally in the profits accruing from the new process. While Smith had done virtually the whole of the work in inventing and developing the process, Urban was just the man to bring the

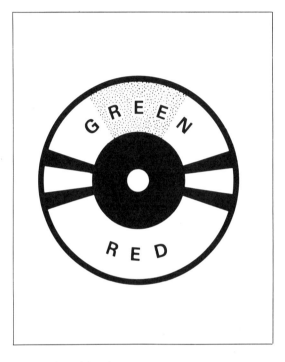

14 Filter disc of the Kinemacolor projector.
The shaded portion of
the green sector
represents a double
thickness of gelatin.

12 Two Kinemacolor
demonstration films
(35 mm).

13 The Kinemacolor
film of the Coronation
of King George V.

15 Henry W. Joy.

colour films before the public. He had by now settled down in England having married the daughter of a Glasgow University professor. He became a naturalised British citizen in 1906. By this time he was probably the most successful man in the industry. The Warwick Trading Company, which he founded, was by 1903 publishing a larger number of films than any other English company. In that year he broke away from the company and formed the Charles Urban Trading Company marketing films and apparatus.

The films made and distributed by the CUTC were mainly travel, natural history and newsreel films. In this respect it was unlike other film companies and reflected Urban's idea that the film was to be an outstanding educational medium. The natural history films in particular were a great success. 'Unseen World', a series of films taken through the microscope by F Martin Duncan, was shown at the Alhambra for a season (1904–5), and received a very warm reception.

In the design of apparatus Urban was assisted after 1905 by Henry W Joy. The Urban-Joy perforator appeared in 1906. The Urban-Joy anti-firing device, a shutter to prevent the firing of inflammable film when projectors broke down, was another of their inventions.

The first demonstration of Kinemacolor took place on May 1st, 1908 on the occasion of the inauguration of Urbanora House, the luxurious new premises of the CUTC in Wardour Street. The audience were mainly newspapermen. *The Morning Post* described the demonstration as 'The great photographic event of the moment.' *The Daily Telegraph* as 'A remarkable advance'. A further

THE PALACE THEATRE OF VARIETIES

Managing Director   -   -   Mr. ALFRED BUTT.

26/2/1909.

FRIDAY, FEBRUARY 26th, 1909, at 3 p.m.

SPECIAL INVITATION MATINÉE.

The First Presentation of

"KINEMACOLOR"

URBAN-SMITH NATURAL COLOUR KINEMATOGRAPHY

(Animated Scenes and Moving Objects Bioscoped in the Actual Tints of Nature).

PROGRAMME.

Overture   ...   .   "Di Ballo"   ...   .   Sullivan.

1. **Representatives of the British Isles** (England, Ireland, Wales, Scotland and Group).
2. **View of Brighton Front** from West Pier.
3. **Band of Queen's Highlanders** on West Pier.
4. **Incident on Brighton Beach.**
5. **The Letter** (showing most difficult tests for colour photography, namely *Grey*).
6. **Sailing and Motor Boat Scenes at Southwick.** (Note effect of sunshine on varnish of Boat rounding the Buoy.)

Slight pause to permit of the spools being changed.

7. **Carnival Scenes at Nice and Cannes.** (Taken Sunday, February 21st, 1909.)
8. **Riviera Coast Scenes.**, Panoramas of Cannes, Nice and Monte Carlo, including Street Incidents.
9. **"Waves and Spray"** (Three Examples of Rocky Coast Scenery).

"Collection" by the Orchestra—

    "Now and Then"   ...   *Arranged by Herman Finck.*

A Pot-pourri of the fascinating airs which have haunted the memories of music lovers during the past century. The tunes range from grave to gay and from lively to severe, and indicate in some degree the variations which have taken place in the public taste.

10. **"Sweet Flowers."** This picture will first be shown as an ordinary Black and White Bioscope view. After an interval of two seconds for adjusting Colour Filters to the Urban Bioscope Machine, **this same picture** will be shown in its natural hues and tints.
11. **The Rabbits.—Sheep.—A Carrot for the Donkey.**
12. **Swans.**
13. **Reaping.**
14. **A Visit to Aldershot.**—The Guard at Government House.
15. **A Detachment of Gordon Highlanders.**
16. **Church Parade of the 7th Hussars and 16th Lancers.**
17. **Soldiers' Pet.**

Slight pause to permit of the spools being changed.

18. **Riviera Fisher Folk.**
19. **Cascade de Courmes, France.**
20. **Children's Battle of Flowers, Nice** (Sunday, February 21st, 1909).
21. **Water Carnival at Villefranche.** As this picture affords special opportunities for colour effects, it is hoped that the audience will remain to witness it.

The Incidental Music played by the Palace Orchestra under the direction of Mr. HERMAN FINCK.

On and after Monday next the Palace Programme will include—

A SELECTION OF THESE PICTURES,

MISS MAUD ALLAN,

LOUIS CALVERT & COMPANY, ARTHUR PRINCE,

MELVILLE ELLIS, LAS FLORIDOS, THE MILLER BROTHERS,

etc., etc., etc.

BOX OFFICE open from 10 a.m. to 11 p.m.   TELEPHONE No. 6834 GERRARD (2 lines)

MATINÉE AT REDUCED PRICES EVERY SATURDAY AT 2.

POPULAR PRICES.—PRIVATE BOXES, 1, 2 and 3 Guineas. FAUTEUILS (numbered and reserved) 7/6. ORCHESTRA STALLS (numbered and reserved), 5/-. ROYAL CIRCLE (numbered and reserved) 5/-. ROYAL CIRCLE (unreserved) 3/- FIRST CIRCLE, 2/-. AMPHITHEATRE 1/-.

Musical Director—Mr. HERMAN FINCK.   Acting Manager—Mr. E. A. PICKERING.

Treasurer—Mr. THOMAS MILLER.   Stage Manager—Mr. FRANK DAMER.

NOTICE.—The Public can leave the Theatre at the end of the performance by all exit and entrance doors which open outwards. All gangways, passages and staircases must be kept free from chairs or any other obstructions. Persons must not be permitted to stand or sit in any of the intersecting gangways, and if standing be permitted in the gangways at the sides and rear of the seating, sufficient space must be left for persons to pass easily to and fro. The safety curtain must be lowered about the middle of the performance so as to ensure its being in proper working order.

---

demonstration was given to the Lord Mayor of London, the sheriffs of London and civic dignitaries on July 23rd, 1908. At this time very little Kinemacolor film was in existence and the demonstrations consisted of a few experimental samples.

The most important of these early demonstrations accompanied a lecture given by Smith before an audience at the Royal Society of Arts on December 9th, 1908. The lecture was reprinted in the Society's journal. This demonstration was considered important by Smith and Urban as they hoped that by lecturing on the subject before a distinguished society the process would gain respect as a scientific advance, instead of being regarded as an entertaining novelty.

By this time Smith had slightly modified the method of projection described in the patent. It was impossible to get a true grey or white by mixing the two colours red and green. The third primary, blue, was needed. In the patent the rotating shutter of the projector consisted of red and green filters separated by opaque wings which masked the projector light while the film was moving. By substituting an additional dark blue or violet filter for each of these opaque portions of the shutter Smith found that he was able to improve the overall colour rendering of the films. When the projector was run without film, the screen appeared white. This method of introducing the third primary, blue, into the pictures may not have been very successful for it appears to have been abandoned when Kinemacolor entered the cinema houses.

Although the variety of Kinemacolor films was very limited, the management of the Palace

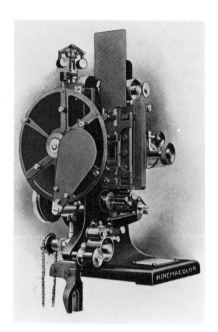

17 Kinemacolor projector (rear). The filter disc comes between the light source and the film. The 'dogs' which advance the film intermittently appear immediately below the film gate.

18 Kinemacolor projector (front view).

Theatre, Shaftesbury Avenue under Alfred Butt (later Sir Alfred Butt) who was present at the Urbanora House demonstrations, signed a contract with Urban to exhibit Kinemacolor before the public. The opening display took the form of a special matinée on February 26th, 1909. This was the first public cinema exhibition of colour moving pictures by a process which did not depend on hand or mechanical colouring. Following this successful opening a Kinemacolor item was included in the daily programme at the theatre for the next eighteen consecutive months from March 1st, 1909. For the first time Urban began to get a return on his investment.

In March 1909 Urban set up the Natural Color Kinematograph Company to handle the production and distribution of Kinemacolor films. Smith's interests in the process were bought for £5000, but his services were retained for a further five years at a fee of £500 a year.

During 1909 Kinemacolor projectors were made by fitting the rotating colour disc shutter to an ordinary Urban bioscope projector and running it at double speed. This was an unsatisfactory arrangement and resulted in excessive wear on the film. In the conventional bioscope projector the film is moved intermittently by what is known as 'dog' motion. The film below the film gate is struck by a revolving eccentric roller or dog which moves the film along the length of one frame. For Kinemacolor films shown at twice the normal speed this movement needed modification and the special projectors, designed by Joy and introduced in March 1910, had a dog which was composed of two eccentric rollers. One of these rollers is placed very near to the central line of the

19 The inside of a Kinemacolor camera. The
twin claw intermittent
movement can be
seen.

20 Kinemacolor camera
made by Moy and
Bastie. The lens panel
and shutter have been
removed to show the
two-colour filter disc.

dog shaft and so describes a small circle; the other,
known as the main dog, is placed in the usual
position. The small dog strikes the film before the
main dog and disturbs the film from rest immediately before it is struck by the main dog. This has
the effect of relieving the strain on the film and so
prolonging its life.

The Kinemacolor projector was heavier and more
substantially built than conventional machines to
reduce vibration which would otherwise occur
during the double speed operation. In British
theatres and cinema houses the Kinemacolor
projector was never hand-operated but was
always attached to a motor which governed the
speed. For New York, where motor driven
machines were apparently against regulations in
1910, a specially geared machine was produced
which could be turned by hand without too much
fatigue.

The Kinemacolor cameras (made by Moy and
Bastie) were conventional bioscope cameras
fitted with a synchronised filter shutter. As the
negative film was run through the camera once
only there was no need to modify the intermittent
mechanism to reduce film wear.

With interest in Kinemacolor growing Urban
resigned from his position as managing director of
the CUTC in January, 1910 to devote all his time to
exploiting Kinemacolor. In England Kinemacolor
could still be seen in only one theatre – the Palace,
London; but in the spring the first colour performances were given in the provinces. Nottingham
and Blackpool were the first provincial towns
to see Kinemacolor, on March 24th, 1910.

The Kinemacolor film of the funeral of King Edward VII provided a breakthrough in that it was a news subject that cinemagoers wanted to see in colour. It was shown in Glasgow, Derby, Nottingham, Blackpool and Burton-on-Trent in May 1910. In June Kinemacolor arrived at Leicester and Birmingham.

A Kinemacolor headquarters (80–82 Wardour Street) was opened on June 1st, 1910. In September 1910 the Natural Color Kinematograph Company issued a 96-page Kinemacolor handbook publicising the new machines which were now available for exhibitors. The subjects of Kinemacolor films were still topical newsreels such as royal events, Ascot and Richmond Horseshow.

Although a Kinemacolor item was included each night at the Palace Theatre, it still remained predominantly a music-hall. Urban now had sufficient Kinemacolor film to put on a complete Kinemacolor programme and looked around for a London theatre which he could convert into the first Kinemacolor cinema. The only one he could lease was the Scala, not entirely to his liking as he did not think it was in a very good position (off Tottenham Court Road) and was rather smaller than he would have liked, seating 920. He was not used to doing things by halves.

The opening performance at the Scala took place on April 11th, 1911. The highlights of the programme at the cinema during the first few months were news events such as the unveiling of the Queen Victoria Memorial (May), the Coronation (June), the Naval Review (June), and the Investiture of the Prince of Wales at Caernarvon (July). The usual policy in the cinemas of the day of a weekly or twice weekly change of programme was disregarded and programmes ran for two months or more. The first Kinemacolor dramas and comedy films were now being produced at studios in Hove, Sussex during the summer months and at Nice, France during the winter. The actors and actresses were the twelve members of a repertory company employed by the Natural Color Kinematograph Company.

In October 1911 the *Bioscope* wrote of the 'almost sensational advance of Kinemacolor'. 'Within the year – almost within the last six months – Mr Charles Urban's Kinemacolor process has come right to the front, and has become a formative influence upon the future of the business, the importance of which cannot be overestimated. "Colour" has become the *sine qua non* of the picture theatre programme, and one cannot pass along the streets without seeing from the announcements of exhibitors that they are fully alive to this, and, if they have not a Kinemacolor licence, they are making a special feature of tinted or coloured films in order to cope with public demand.'

Kinemacolor's greatest success came in the following year with a 16 000 feet (two and a half hour) film of the Delhi Durbar of 1911 which opened at the Scala on February 2nd, 1912. This was an ideal subject for the process with plenty of colour and pageantry under the bright sun in Bombay, Delhi and Calcutta. This was the first time a cinema audience had been expected to sit through a two and a half hour film on one subject; the longest films produced before 1912 were three reels in length lasting 45 to 60 minutes.

21 Kinemacolor House.
The perforating room
which had twenty
machines.

22 Kinemacolor House.
A section of the film
printing room which
had twenty printing
machines.

23 Kinemacolor House.
Film developing on pin
frames. Operators
worked in a very faint
green light, not in
absolute darkness.

24 Kinemacolor House.
The film drying room.
There were two drying
rooms, each with five
drums.

*Typewritten notes dated 1921 in the Science Museum Urban Collection.

'The Birth of a Nation' (first shown at the Scala in 1915) and other big feature films were still several years away.

Urban's own account of the production of the film is as follows:* 'We were met in India by Sir John Hewitt who had charge of all arrangements re the Durbar etc, he gave me a half hour to tell what we required but drove about with me the entire afternoon in order to select the positions I wanted. He was as fascinated as anyone. It is worthy for the sake of the record to say the principal cameraman was Joseph de Frene.

'We had the choicest of all possible positions, the officials afforded us the best of protection. They had heard rumors that rival film companies were bent on damaging or destroying our pictures and inasmuch as the King expected to see these pictures in London, it was up to the Army to see that we got them safely there. Each night we used to develop the negatives exposed during the day, and bury them in cases dug in the sand in my tent with a piece of linoleum and a rug on top of them, a pistol under my pillow and armed guards patrolling my camp.

'When I arrived in London one month after our competitors had hurried after the Delhi ceremonies (I went to Calcutta after the Elephant Pageant) I was met on every side with cries of derision.

"Your stuff is old; Everybody has seen the Durbar and is tired of it". But they had seen it only in monotone and I had no fear of the reception of the pictures in Natural color. I had a special stage setting of the Taj Mahal built, special music written for the presentation of the pictures.

Arrangements went ahead steadily and when the time came we opened in magnificence. I dare say that our presentation of Kinemacolor was the beginning of the splendid presentations in picture houses today [1921] . . .

'The augmented orchestra – 48 pieces, the chorus of 24, a fife and drum corps of 20, 3 Scotch bag-pipes and beautiful electrical effects – we had all these.

'It was a brilliant opening and a splendid financial success. We sent out five road shows in England, Ireland, Scotland and Wales, always, mind you, following where black and white pictures of the same subjects had been previously shown.

'In fifteen months we grossed more than £150,000 after the interests in the monochrome production were exhausted in three weeks.'

At the Prince's Theatre, Manchester the week's takings of the Durbar series were £1700, a Manchester record.

The Morning Post wrote 'It is quite safe to say nothing so stirring, so varied, so beautiful, so stupendous, as these moving pictures, all in their natural colours, has ever been seen before.

Kinemacolor was unable to repeat the success of the Delhi Durbar film with any of its dramatic productions or photoplays. Of these productions although the colour was almost invariably praised, it was said 'the acting was poor and the direction worse'. 'Mephisto' (1912) was a film about the evils of greed, gambling, drink and lust, which was accompanied by Gounod's 'Faust'. 'Oedipus Rex'

88822295047258669994610944

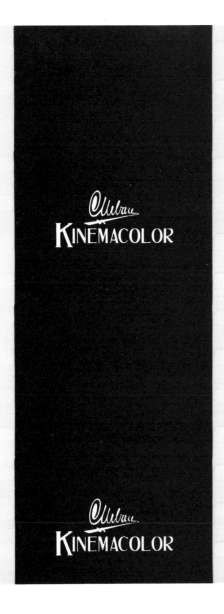

Left:
25 Kinemacolor title.
The letters appear on
alternate frames. The
film was threaded so
that the letters
appeared in red on the
screen. This ensured
that the 'red' series of
frames was synchron-
ised with the red
portion of the filter
disc and the 'green'
series with the green
portion. If the letters
did not appear red on
the screen the mask
on the projector was
realigned until they
did. The arc was then
recentred to provide
the brightest
illumination.

Right:
26 The Kinemacolor of
America title. At the
centre is the two-
colour rotating filter
disc.

THE WORLD THE FLESH AND THE DEVIL
By LAURENCE COWEN.

Reproduced

with

Stereoscopic

Relief

in

Four Parts

120 Scenes

Matinees only
Daily, 2.30 to 5 p.m.

The escape from the Mill.

THE HOLBORN EMPIRE

A

100

Minute

Thrill

The

Greatest

Photo-Play

in London

Prices:
6d. to 5s.

(3705 feet) was another of their productions filmed at Nice. 'The World the Flesh and the Devil', a 100-minute film, was put on at the Holborn Empire in 1914. Four more of their longer dramatic films were 'The Scarlet Letter' (3 reels 4370 feet), 'Robin Hood, (4475 feet), 'Dr Jekyll and Mr Hyde' (two reels), and 'Vandal Outlaws' (2410 feet).

Apart from the Delhi Durbar the longest non-fiction production was 'The Opening of the Panama Canal' (9 reels, 11 000 feet) which opened at the Scala in October 1912.

In 1913 a new studio for Kinemacolor was built in a meadow behind Urban's mansion at Bushey Park, 14 miles from the centre of London. This had a revolving stage which always faced the sun, pinpointing the need for good lighting for filming by the Kinemacolor process.

There were several noteworthy performances which deserve a mention. The first time royalty saw Kinemacolor was on July 6th, 1909, when King Edward VII and Queen Alexandra, at the invitation of the Earl of Derby, attended a show at Knowsley. Smith was presented to the King. On July 29th, 1911, a Command Performance of Kinemacolor was given at Sandringham before Queen Alexandra. On September 14th and 15th, 1911, Kinemacolor films of the Coronation and of the Investiture of the Prince of Wales at Caernarvon were shown at Balmoral.

On May 11th, 1912, King George V, Queen Mary, Queen Alexandra and the Dowager Empress of Russia visited the Scala to see the Delhi Durbar films.

Presented by **KINEMACOLOR**
A £10,000 Picture Play in Actual Colors.

A
MELO-DRAMA
seething
with
Sensations.

—

Don't
miss
it !

—

Box Office
Tel.: 5367 Holborn.

Also
amazing
Programme
of the
World's
Wonders
in
Nature's
Colors.

—

"Drink, to the World the Flesh and the Devil!"

THE HOLBORN EMPIRE

Matinees only

Daily, 2.30 to 5 p.m.

27 From a folder publicising 'The World, the Flesh and the Devil' (1914).

The Emperor of Japan saw Kinemacolor at his palace in Tokyo during August, 1913. A special Kinemacolor performance was given to the Pope at the Vatican in June, 1913.

Kinemacolor Abroad

FRANCE
The first demonstrations of Kinemacolor took place in Paris in July, 1908 and April, 1909. France was the centre for hand and stencil coloured films and Urban feared that his process might be mistaken for a new hand-colouring process. But hand-colouring usually took several weeks and to show that the new films were made by a different and better process, the Grand Prix Motor Race at Dieppe was filmed and the film was shown in colour to the audience the day after the race took place.

In 1912 the patents for France were sold to the Paris firm Raleigh and Robert, who exhibited Kinemacolor films at the American Biograph Theatre, Rue de Peletier, during 1912 and 1913. When they tried to extend their operations they failed because, according to Urban, they asked exhorbitant prices. The Natural Color Kinematograph Company repurchased the French patents at a loss.

The success of Kinemacolor at the Scala led Urban to believe that he could repeat this in Paris. In 1912 he purchased the lease of a premises in the Rue Edouard VII, Boulevard des Capucines, and built the Théâtre Edouard VII. The theatre, seating 800, was sumptuously furnished and opened on December 12th, 1913. This venture proved a failure and was said to have cost Urban £45 000. The theatre was smaller than the Scala, charged higher prices, and was not in a very good site. It closed for the summer in May 1914 and was still closed at the outbreak of war. Urban finally disposed of the lease to a Parisian theatrical manager.

UNITED STATES

Kinemacolor was first shown in the United States at Madison Square Garden, New York City, before an audience of 1200 on December 11th, 1909. As a result of this very successful demonstration Urban sold the United States patents outright for £40000. The Kinemacolor Company of America was set up in the spring of 1910 centred at Allentown, Pennsylvania. The American company ran into many difficulties at first but by April 1913 the F F Proctor chain of cinemas were showing Kinemacolor and in that month William Fox contracted to show Kinemacolor in his cinemas. Previously a great many exhibitors who had wished to show colour films had been deterred by threats that, if they did, their supplies of black and white films would be discontinued.

During the three or four years that the Kinemacolor Company of America was operative, nine Kinemacolor cameras were employed, a quarter of a million feet of negative film was shot and eighty or ninety Kinemacolor projectors were rented.

Nevertheless Kinemacolor failed in the United States. Urban always regretted that he did not retain an interest in Kinemacolor in America and believed that with better management it would have been a huge success.

ELSEWHERE

The patents for Italy were sold for £8000 in 1912, but due to opposition from the whole of the motion picture industry producing black and white films, operations ceased about nine months later.

The Kinemacolor Company of Japan, which purchased the Japanese rights for £10000 in September 1913, was quite successful and was operating seven special Kinemacolor theatres in Tokyo by the outbreak of the war.

Patent rights were also sold in Russia and Finland (£20000), in Canada (£10000), in Holland and Belgium (£6000), in Brazil (£2000), and in Switzerland (£2500). In none of these countries did Kinemacolor achieve any great success.

The Limitations of Kinemacolor

Kinemacolor succeeded in bringing something new to the motion picture industry and it was a commercial success. Nevertheless it had some limitations which are worth noting.

The films were taken at twice the speed of black and white films. The maximum exposure which could be given to each frame was therefore only half that of black and white cinematography. Also light reached the film through the rotating colour filters which again seriously reduced the exposure. Thus Kinemacolor films could only be taken under very good light conditions – in fact good sunlight. Film studios were increasingly using artificial lighting to replace and supplement natural light, and after 1912 the artificial light was often the

Cooper-Hewitt mercury vapour lamp introduced from America. This was particularly strong in blue-violet light and very weak in red and green; quite suitable for black and white filming but useless for Kinemacolor or any other colour process.

As about 70 per cent of Kinemacolor film was non-fiction film (newsreel or travel film) shot out of doors, this limitation may not have appeared very serious to Urban, who was primarily interested in this type of film. In 1910 he wrote 'With the life and scenery of the world, in every land upon which the sun shines, waiting to be recorded in color, time spent in finding ways and means of photographing artificial comedies or artificial tragedies by artificial light is wasted'. The difficulty of filming in artificial light was however a serious hindrance to the general adoption of Kinemacolor in other studios where a very high proportion of films produced were comedies or dramas.

The loss of light resulting from projection through filters (a feature of all additive motion picture processes) was also a drawback. With the normal projection illuminant this would result in a dim picture on the screen unless the size of screen was reduced. In fact Kinemacolor operators were advised to use a smaller screen than usual to maintain the level of illumination at that to which cinemagoers had become accustomed.

The most serious defect of the Kinemacolor process resulted in fringing. A period of time of about 1/30th of a second elapsed between the 'red' exposure and the 'green' exposure in the camera. During this time interval some movement of the subject took place with the result that the two consecutive exposures produced frames which were not identical and so perfect registration or superimposition on the screen was impossible. Coloured fringes were seen around moving objects. The effect was only annoying however when a player approached to within six or seven feet of the lens and when the direction of movement was directly across the field of view.

Prolonged viewing of Kinemacolor produced eye-strain resulting from the projection of the two colour records near the threshold frequency needed for persistence of vision to combine the two colours. For some people this resulted in discomfort and headaches.

Projection of Kinemacolor films needed a special expensive projector which exhibitors hired for the performance. One report which Urban received said: 'It is absolutely necessary to have a machine which will project both black and white and Kinemacolor films so as to obviate the trouble and unnecessary expense of taking a special Kinemacolor machine each time Kinemacolor films are shown. Further, there are not many theatres or cinema houses where there is room for an additional machine, therefore, before a Kinemacolor show can be given, the existing machine has to be dismantled and the Kinemacolor machine set up in its place. Cinema proprietors do not like to go to all this trouble'.

As Kinemacolor film was run at twice the normal speed through both camera and projector, the cost of filming was at least twice that of filming in black and white. The additional wear on the film reduced the life of Kinemacolor prints considerably and made breakdowns more frequent. When a film broke, care had to be taken in splicing to

28 Adjacent advertise-
ments from a South
African newspaper
(1915). Two drawbacks
of Kinemacolor were
the eyestrain of which
some viewers com-
plained and the lack of
variety of programmes.

EMPIRE THEATRE

Sub-Lesees—EMPIRE CINEMA CO.

Enormous Success, Unparalleled Enthusiasm Unanimous Opinion.

KINEMACOLOR

Is the Greatest thing ever seen in the world of Cinematography.

KINEMACOLOR

Can be seen only at the Empire.

KINEMACOLOR

Has been installed at a cost of over £500.

PALACE THEATRE

W. R. PATERSON, PROPRIETOR.

The Amusement Sanatorium.

When you're colour blind, and y ur head aches, and you want relief and variety of amusement, come to the Palace where they change every night, and guarantee the Best.

TO-NIGHT'S PROGRAMME.

THE DARLING OF THE C.S.A.

(Powerful " Kalem " Military Drama).

AN INDIAN'S GRATITUDE

(Lubin Drama).

GAUMONT'S GRAPHIC

ensure that two red or two green frames were not spliced together.

The Kinemacolor library of films was never large enough to provide a theatre with a twice weekly change of programme and was deficient in comedy and drama, the mainstay of all cinema programmes from 1896 to the present time. When Kinemacolor came to an end in 1916 the library in the basement vaults in Wardour Street contained nearly 700 000 feet of Kinemacolor negatives

(equivalent to 80–90 hours continuous projection). More than half of this was of travel, educational and news subjects; 90 000 feet was classified as children's films or trick films; less than 200 000 feet was 'dramatic and humorous'.

Kinemacolor, being a two-colour process, could not of course reproduce the full range of colours of the spectrum. The colour reproduction would appear very poor to audiences of to-day accustomed to the three-colour subtractive processes of the cinema and the three-colour additive process of colour television. But before World War 1 it was the only natural colour process to achieve public exhibition and there was almost universal praise for the range of colours. Three-colour prints only appeared in the cinema after 1930 (Technicolor), and indeed films using two-colour processes (e.g. Cinecolor) were still being produced up to about 1950.

Kinemacolor in the Law Courts

During the three years April 1911 to March 1914 Kinemacolor's total receipts were nearly £300 000. Expenditure was about £260 000, profit was about £37 000. Over £100 000 was received from the sale of patent rights abroad. Licence fees for foreign exhibition rights brought in another £21 000.

In Britain the gross receipts from the two year run at the Scala were £65 000. The hire of machines to provincial theatres (Kinemacolor was shown at nearly 300 theatres and picture houses in Britain outside London) brought in £32 000. Exhibition fees from London district theatres brought in nearly £11 000.

The success of Kinemacolor naturally led competitors to examine ways of producing motion pictures in colour. Unfortunately for them there appeared no simple method of producing the result without infringing Smith's patent. William Friese-Greene in particular felt ill-fated for he had patented a two-colour process the year before Smith, but his process had proved impossible to put into practice.

Friese-Greene, supported by the financier S F Edge, then attacked Smith's patent with the intention of getting it revoked. Bioschemes Ltd, a company financed by Edge, objected to Smith's patent on the grounds that it was not detailed enough and on the grounds that the process had been used by others before Smith. In particular they claimed that the patent did not state what colour red and what colour green filters were to be used on the camera and projector, no method of sensitising the film emulsion was given, and also they claimed that the patent was incorrect in stating that the process gave an approximately correct rendering of natural colours as blue was absent from the results.

The petition was heard in the High Court on December 8–15th, 1913. Each side managed to produce a Professor of Physics who was also a Fellow of the Royal Society to give evidence, Professor S P Thompson for the Natural Color Kinematograph Company, Professor C V Boys for Bioschemes. The evidence took up 300 pages and is impossible to summarise adequately in any convenient length. On December 19th, 1913, the judge dismissed the petition of Bioschemes and the Natural Color Kinematograph Company had won the first round. Bioschemes appealed against the verdict. The Court of Appeal sat on March 20th, 23rd and 24th, 1914. The appeal was granted and the first judgement reversed. The appeals judge said: 'The matter may be summarised thus: The patentee says his process will reproduce the natural colours or approximately so. Blue is a colour. He says: Drop the tricolour blue; do not employ the blue end of the spectrum – blue or approximately blue will still be reproduced. It will not. The patent is consequently invalid'.

The question of prior use or prior publication was not discussed by the appeals judge.

The Natural Color Kinematograph Company took the dispute to the House of Lords where the decision of the Court of Appeal was upheld and so Bioschemes had won. The final decision came in March, 1915. This was not of course the end of Kinemacolor. From this date the process was not protected by patent and was freely available to all. However, probably because of the War, the process was not exploited by anyone in Britain other than Urban.

Post Kinemacolor

After the outbreak of war in August 1914, Urban went to the United States to help publicise the British war effort by means of films. Without Urban's management Kinemacolor in England gradually declined until after 1916, the process became defunct.

The Urban-Joy Process (Kinekrom)

In America Urban was still keenly interested in natural colour processes for motion pictures but, having sold out his interests in Kinemacolor patents to Kinemacolor of America, he was unable to foster Kinemacolor and instead attempted to promote an improved process which was devised by Henry Joy. (Smith and Urban had fallen out as soon as Kinemacolor achieved success and Smith found that he had disposed of his interest in the patent for what he believed was too low a price.)

The most serious defect in Kinemacolor films was, as we have seen, the fringing which resulted from the time interval between taking the red colour record and the green colour record. The ideal solution to this problem was to take both records simultaneously by means of a beam-splitting system. With such a system light entering the camera lens is divided by means of a mirror or prism into two beams, each beam producing a colour record after passing through the appropriate filter. Beam-splitting cameras had been successfully used for still colour photography from the early 1900s and were to be successful for motion picture colour photography after 1920.

However, Joy, who was interested in mechanics rather than optics, believed that beam-splitting systems would never be practicable for motion picture cameras and instead designed an improved Kinemacolor camera in which the time interval between taking the red record and the green record was halved by means of an improved intermittent mechanism. This reduced, but did not remove, the defect of fringing and did nothing to obviate the other limitations of Kinemacolor. The Urban-Joy process, or Kinekrom as it was called, was promoted in the United States but never got beyond experimental demonstrations. From Urban's point of view, if the Urban-Joy process had caught on, he would have been able to utilise the millions of feet of Kinemacolor negative and positive film which was still in existence in the film libraries and which could be projected with the Kinekrom projectors; but this never came about.

The Gaumont Chronochrome Process

During the brief life of Kinemacolor there were no natural colour processes to provide any serious competition. One three-colour process, Chronochrome, appeared on the horizon in 1912–1913, but it failed to be exploited commercially.

Chronochrome negatives were obtained in a camera equipped with three lenses, placed one above the other, each fitted with a glass filter. The negative produced consisted of red, green and blue colour records, each colour record recurring every third frame. Three images, one the red record, one the green record and the third the blue record, were simultaneously projected through three lenses fitted with filters to produce a natural colour picture on the screen. In this respect it resembles the Lee and Turner process. During projection the projection lenses and filters had to

29 Kinekrom camera filter disc.

be carefully aligned to produce the screen image as accurately in register as possible. This was effected by moving the top and bottom lenses in three directions by an alignment mechanism, the middle lens being fixed.

If the size of each frame had been the same as that of standard 35 mm film each scene would have required three times the length of film ordinarily used and the film would have had to have been moved very rapidly in both camera and projector. However, the height of the frames was reduced by one quarter. This reduced the film length to about two and a half times that of black and white film and lessened the strain imposed on the film.

The film in both camera and projector was moved three frames at a time which necessitated the development of a modified intermittent movement capable of a very long pulldown without undue strain on the film. At first there were difficulties in sensitising film stock to red and green light. (This makes Smith's feat in sensitising film stock for Kinemacolor all the more remarkable.) The projection speed needed to be 48 frames a second which implied a shorter exposure through the red and green filters than proved practicable. The result was that in early demonstrations the projection speed was greater than the taking speed. As one of the audience put it – '. . . the exhibited pictures showing animation were speeded up until a man leisurely walking appeared to run; and the lazy flight of the sea-gull was the speed of an express train.'

The process was first demonstrated before the French Photographic Society on November 15th 1912. It was first shown in London on January 16th 1913. Urban had two of his associates, Henry Joy (the engineer) and F H Rogers (a patent agent), attend the demonstration. Rogers reported: 'We both came to the conclusion that whilst the results were good, it is a difficult and somewhat un-commercial process at the moment, requiring skill of manipulation to get results, and that the speed of projection either precludes real animation, or entails tremendous wear on the film.

'On the question of Patents, there is very little, if any doubt that the Lee-Turner Patent is infringed. Having regard to the expiring of this patent the month after next, and also the fact that up to the present time they have not attempted to exploit the process commercially, it is questionable whether an action for infringement would be commercially advantageous.'

A further demonstration was given at the 39th Street Theatre, New York City in June, 1913. This time talking pictures (produced by coupling an Elgéphone talking machine to the colour projector) were also demonstrated. George Eastman became interested in the process. However, although demonstrations were given as late as 1920, the process never reached the stage of regular public exhibition.

Prizma

An attempt at improving the Kinemacolor process was made in America by William van Doren Kelly of Prizma Inc. He worked on a number of cameras designed to produce blue-green and red-orange records simultaneously so obviating the coloured fringes of Kinemacolor. One of these cameras used two lenses, one above the other with a separation of three-quarters of an inch. Although this camera overcame the problem of fringing it introduced another defect, that of parallax. The images formed by the two lenses are seen from slightly different viewpoints by each lens and so are not identical and cannot be accurately in register on the screen whatever method of projection is used. Kelly used the Kinemacolor method of projection with a rotating filter on the projector, but with Prizma additive process the filter disc was made up of four colours instead of Kinemacolor's two. The first demonstration of the new Prizma process was given at the American Museum of Natural History, New York on February 8th, 1917. It is doubtful if this process was much superior to Kinemacolor.

Kelly having seen the disadvantages of additive colour processes turned his attention to subtractive colour films, films with a colour image carried on the film itself in the form of dyes, rather than introduced by filters. His negatives were produced in a Kinemacolor type of camera and had the red and green records on alternate frames along the film. For printing positives he used double coated film stock, film which has a sensitive emulsion coating on both back and front of the film base. The film base of such a film is made opaque to printing light by means of an appropriate dye so that when one side of the film is exposed to printing light the light does not penetrate through the base to affect the emulsion on the reverse side. During processing this dye is dissolved out to leave the transparent base between the two emulsions. The orange-red record of the Prizma two colour film was printed on one side of the double coated film, the blue-green record on the other side. If we take the case of the 'red' images,

after one 'red' image has been printed, the positive is moved along one frame while the negative, which has red records alternately along the film, is moved along two frames. When the 'green' images have been printed on the other side of the film we now have the two silver images one on each side of the film and in register. (Note that in order to get both images the same way round one negative must be printed through the negative film base instead of using the usual way of printing emulsion to emulsion.)

Having printed the two colour records on either side of the double coated film stock, the next problem is to convert the black silver images into the appropriate colours, i.e. blue-green and orange-red. One method which Kelly used was chemical toning. This involves converting the silver image on one side of the film into silver ferrocyanide (blue-green) by treatment with potassium ferrocyanide. The silver image on the reverse side was converted into uranium ferrocyanide (orange-red) or, alternatively, into silver iodide which is a mordant for basic dyes. The film was treated with the necessary reagents by floating it on top of the reagent solutions. In this way only one side of the film was affected by each particular reagent.

An alternative method of producing the images in the appropriate colour was to harden the gelatin in which the image is embedded in proportion to the amount of silver present. Leon Warnecke, a Pole who lived in England, had published a method by which this could be done in 1881. He had found that when a gelatin film is developed by a pyrogallol developer in the absence of sulphite, the oxidation products of the developer

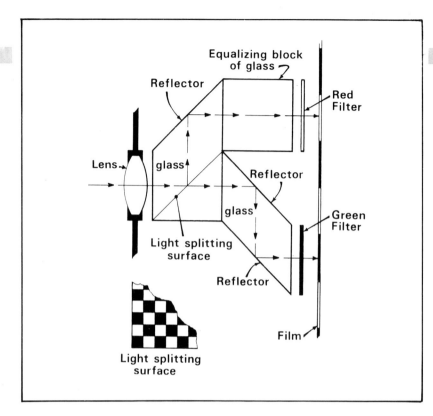

Equalizing block
of glass

Reflector

Red
Filter

Lens

glass

Reflector

glass

Green
Filter

Light splitting
surface

Reflector

Film

Light splitting
surface

30 Sectional diagram of an early Technicolor camera (c. 1920).

harden or tan the gelatin. As the oxidation products are produced in proportion to the density of the silver image, the method produces an 'image' of hardened gelatin. The silver in the image can be dissolved away by a reagent known as Farmer's reducer. The hardened portions of the gelatin which remain can provide a coloured image by the selective action of dyes, i.e. the film is treated with the appropriate dyes, blue-green on one side, orange-red on the other, which are only absorbed by the hardened parts of the gelatin.

The first feature film made by the Prizma subtractive process was 'The Glorious Adventure' starring Lady Diana Manners, a film of the Fire of London shot at Cricklewood, England in 1921. The cost of

prints of the film was 25 cents a foot, about six times the cost of black and white prints at the time.

The Prizma subtractive process was not an immediate success; but it did form the basis of later successful two-colour processes, such as Cinecolor, Multicolor and Trucolor, as toning and dyeing of double coated stock proved to be one of the cheapest of colour printing techniques.

Early Technicolor

The Technicolor Motion Picture Corporation was founded in 1915 by Herbert Kalmus, Daniel Frost Comstock and W Burton Westcott. In the early stages they were financed by a former New York District Attorney, William Jerome Travers and by New York businessmen. Until 1930 Technicolor used a two-colour system and from the very start their two colour records were obtained simultaneously (not, like the Kinemacolor system, consecutively). One of their early cameras for obtaining simultaneous two-colour records had a beam-splitting mirror made up of squares of silver alternating with squares of clear glass (like the squares of a draughtsboard). Light striking the silvered squares was reflected to give the red record, light striking the clear squares was transmitted to give the green record. The film in the camera was moved forward two frames at a time and the exposed and processed film carried alternate red and green records as did Kinemacolor negative film.

One disadvantage of this early Technicolor camera was that light passed through about three and a half inches of glass between the lens and the film and some of it was absorbed by the glass.

Another disadvantage was that, because of the size of the beam-splitting system behind the lens, the focal length of the lens was of necessity as much as four inches, considerably longer than the normal focal length of 35 mm cine lenses.

At first the Technicolor Motion Picture Corporation worked with an additive projection system using a projector equipped with filters. The projector projected two images, one green, one red, and the two images were brought into register on the screen by means of a thin glass element in front of the projector.

In 1917 the first Technicolor film was produced – 'The Gulf Between'. This was processed in a railway carriage laboratory in Florida. Although the colours of this additive two-colour film were praised, the projection system had its defects and Kalmus is reported as saying 'I concluded that the operator would have to be a cross between a university professor and an acrobat'.* This first Technicolor film was also their last additive film. Charles Urban was present at the screening of this first Technicolor production and wrote a very condescending letter ('I may be able to give you a few tips') welcoming the Technicolor Corporation to the industry. This was probably the last condescending letter they received from a competitor for very many years. After 1917 Technicolor films were made by subtractive processes in which the colour was carried on the film itself, processes which have little relationship to Kinemacolor.

31 A selection of Kinemacolor Programmes.

*H T Kalmus: *Journal of the Society of Motion Picture Engineers,* Vol. XXXI, pp. 564–585, 1938.

Kinemacolor programmes

These programmes can be found in the Science Museum and its Library

Sandringham	29th July, 1911
Balmoral	September, 1911
Buckingham Palace	12th February, 1912

Public Performances

Berlin	Winter-Garten	22nd March, 1909
		23 March, 1909
		11th December, 1909
		6th January, 1910
	Neues Konigl. Operntheater	undated (1910)
	Passage Theater	11th November, 1912
Cambridge	Guildhall	23rd October, 1913
Glasgow	Charing Cross Electric Theatre	12th May, 1910
London	Scala	11th April, 1911
		24th July, 1911
		11th May, 1912
		12th November, 1912
		16th June, 1913
		26th September, 1914
		various undated
	Palace	26th February, 1909
		2nd March, 1909
		22nd March, 1909
		29th March, 1909
		27th May, 1909
		21st July, 1909

Public Performances: continued

London	Palace	11th October, 1909
		27th May, 1910
		6th June, 1910
	West-End Cinema, Coventry Street	18th November, 1913
	Theatre Royal, Haymarket	11th February, 1915
	Philharmonic Hall	undated (1914)
	Urbanora House	23rd July, 1908
	New Gallery Kinema, Regent St. Quadrant	2nd February, 1913
	Holborn Empire	9th April, 1914
Lyons	Théâtre de la Scala	6th October, 1909
Madrid	Gran Teatro y Cinema X	11th November, 1915
Manchester	Midland Theatre	undated (1911)
Melbourne	The Auditorium	9th February, 1914
Montreal	Family Theatre	25th March, 1912
Newcastle-upon-Tyne	Pavilion	undated (1911)
New York	Madison Square Garden	December 11th, 1909
	New York Theatre	undated (1912)
Nottingham	Victoria Electric Palace	March, 1910
Paris	Folies Bergère	4th September, 1909
	Théâtre Edouard VII	12th December, 1913
		13th March, 1914
	American Biograph	undated

Bibliography

Kinemacolor

Colin N Bennett: On Operating Kinemacolor, pp25 (1910)

Natural Color Kinematograph Company Ltd. v Bioschemes Ltd. On Appeal in the House of Lords. Appendix. pp404 (1915)

Kinemacolor Handbook, September, 1910. pp96

* G A Smith: Animated Photographs in Natural Colours, *Journal of the Royal Society of Arts,* Vol LVII, 11th December, 1908, pp70–76

Explanatory Lecture on the Pageants, Processions and Ceremonies Connected with the Imperial Durbar at Delhi as Reproduced by Kinemacolor for use at the Scala Theatre. Compiled and Arranged by St John Hamund, 1912, pp25

† Kinemacolor Catalogue of films, 1912–13

Kinemacolor Films 1915–16. pp24

Charles Urban: Terse History of Natural Colour Kinematography, pp14 (1921)

* C E K Mees: Three-Colour Kinematography, *Nature,* Vol LXXXVII, (1911), p556

* Colin N Bennett: Filter Absorptions for Two-Colour, *British Journal of Photography,* Supplement on Colour Photography, 7th July, 1911, p45

G A Smith: Patent No 26671 of 1906

* Kinemacolor Press Appreciations: British Continental and American, pp240 A scrapbook compiled by C Urban

* Kinemacolor and Some American Criticisms. pp6 (1910)

* W E Smith: The Kinemacolor Process, *The Moving Picture News,* Vol. V, 9th March, 1912, pp12–17

* H W Joy: Instruction for Operators of Kinemacolor Appliances, pp28 (1910)

* Kinemacolor Supplements to the *Kinematograph and Lantern Weekly,* (1912)

For a general history of colour cinematography see 'A History of Motion Picture Color Technology' by R T Ryan (The Focal Press, 1977, London and New York).

For a history of the technology of the cinema see 'A History of Movie Photography' by Brian Coe (Ash & Grant, 1981, London).

Items marked * are in the Science Museum Library. The item marked † is in the Library of the National Film Archive. All other items are in the Science Museum Cinematography Collection.

Apparatus

All the following are contained in the Science Museum collection:

Lee and Turner three-colour projector. (Presented by Charles Urban)

Perforator for Lee and Turner film. (Lent by A Darling)

Urban filter-tinting machine. (Presented by Charles Urban)

Various Kinemacolor colour filters. (Presented by Charles Urban)

Four film boxes for Kinemacolor negative film, used while filming the Delhi Durbar. (Presented by Charles Urban)

Kinemacolor rewinder. (Bequeathed by Mrs K L Smith)

Kinemacolor Camera. (Presented by The Film Producers Guild Ltd)

Printed in the UK for HMSO
Dd 736251 C20 7/83